ACHIEV LEVEL 4

MATHEMATICS
Practice
Questions

Louise Moore

Series Editor: **Richard Cooper**

Rising Stars UK Ltd, 7 Hatchers Mews, Bermondsey Street, London SE1 3GS

www.risingstars-uk.com

All facts are correct at time of going to press.

First published 2003
Second edition 2008
This edition 2010
Reprinted 2011

First edition written by: Richard Cooper
Illustrations: Tim Oliver
Design: Clive Sutherland
Cover design: Burville-Riley Partnership

British Library Cataloguing in Publication Data
A CIP record for this book is available from the British Library.

ISBN 978-1-84680-779-4

Printed by Craft Print International Ltd, Singapore

Contents

The answers can be found in a pull-out section
in the middle of this book.

How to use this book

Level 3 'Tricky Bits' practice questions

1 A set of warm-up practice questions organised by topic. Provides practice in all the Level 3 'Tricky Bits' included in the Achieve Level 4 Maths revision book.

2 Each question has space for your answer. Each question gains a specific number of marks (like a real National Test question). Answers are included in the middle of the book. Marking guidance is provided.

Topic questions

1 Sets of questions on all the topics you need to cover for the Maths National Tests. Each topic includes some questions on Using and applying mathematics.

2 Each question has space for your answer and each answer gains a specific number of marks (like a real National Test question). Answers are included in the middle of the book.

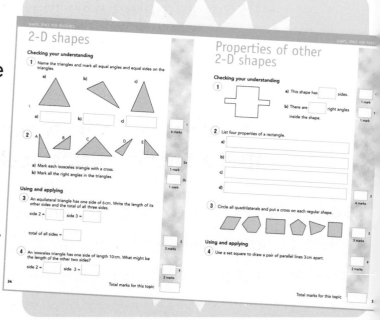

The problem-solving flow chart

(1) Read the question then read it again.

Read the question twice carefully. Let the words and numbers 'sink in'.

(2) Write the numbers and highlight any key words.

Write down any numbers and key words. It might help to draw a picture or diagram.

(3) Can you estimate an answer?

This depends on the question. Try to estimate using the numbers and words you jotted down in step 2.

(4) Which calculations do you need to do?

Work out if you need to use +, −, × or ÷. Check if you need to do more than one calculation.

(5) Look at the numbers. Decide what method to use for your calculations. Is it appropriate to use a calculator? Work out the problem.

Do any calculations needed. Make sure you are answering the problem.

(6) Is your answer sensible?

Read the question again and check that your answer is realistic. If not, go back to step 2.

Tips
* Remember your 'checking the answer' skills.
* Think clearly and write clearly.
* Present your work so it shows what you have done.
* Work step by step.
* Make a problem easier (e.g. 'Find 24 lots of 6'. Try finding 4 lots first then 20 lots.).

* Take a reasonable guess at what you think might happen.
* Think HOW you are working. Change your method if something isn't working.
* Look for patterns in your maths.

Use this flow chart to help you answer questions that involve solving problems (especially using and applying mathematics questions). It provides a step-by-step approach to working through a question, understanding what you need to do to answer it and checking your answer. This is a really useful technique to remember and use when you are sitting the National Test.

Key facts

NUMBER AND ALGEBRA
Counting and understanding number
Place value
- Each number is made up of digits. The position of the digit in a number gives it its value.

Hundreds	Tens	Units	tenths	hundredths
7	8	4	3	5

$$= 700 + 80 + 4 + \frac{3}{10} + \frac{5}{100} = 784.35$$

Estimating
- When rounding, remember 5 goes up! 6.785 rounds up to 6.79.

Positive and negative integers
- Integers are just whole numbers.
- When counting from negative up to positive or from positive down to negative, **remember to count 0!**
- When counting on a number line, count to the right when adding and to the left when subtracting.

Fractions
- A fraction is part of a whole number.

$\frac{1}{2}$ the numerator / the denominator

The numerator tells you how many equal parts are used.
The denominator tells you how many equal parts there are.

Reducing a fraction to its simplest form
- To reduce a fraction to its simplest form, find a common factor which you can divide into the numerator and the denominator. For example,

$$\frac{3 \div 3}{9 \div 3} = \frac{1}{3}$$

Fraction, decimal and percentage equivalents
- Remember as many of these as you can.

Fraction	$\frac{1}{2}$	$\frac{1}{10}$	$\frac{1}{4}$	$\frac{3}{4}$	Nearly $\frac{1}{3}$
Decimal	0.5	0.1	0.25	0.75	0.33
Percentage	50%	10%	25%	75%	33%

The vocabulary of ratio and proportion
- Ratio is 'to every'.
- Proportion is 'in every'.
- Reduce ratios and proportions to their lowest form.

Knowing and using number facts
- **Tables:** it is essential that you know these really well.
- **Squares:** numbers made when a number is multiplied by itself.
- **Multiples:** numbers that have been multiplied by a given number.
- **Factors:** numbers that can divide into a given number without leaving a remainder.

Checking your answers
- Inverse means opposite!
- Check addition by subtraction – and vice versa.
- Check division by multiplication – and vice versa.
- Use 'friendly numbers' when estimating: 2, 5, 10, etc.

Calculating
- Multiplying numbers by 10 and 100: push the digits to the left once for ×10 and twice for ×100.
- Dividing numbers by 10 and 100: push the digits to the right once for ÷10 and twice for ÷100.
- Addition and subtraction of decimals:
  1. Line up the decimal points when you write out the calculation.
  2. Fill empty places with a 0.
  3. Remember to put the decimal point in your answer!

Choosing your method
- Remember to look at the numbers you are working with. You might be able to use a good mental strategy rather than a written method, or it might be best to use a calculator.

SHAPE, SPACE AND MEASURES
Understanding shape
3-D shapes
- Vertices are corners.
- Faces are flat surfaces.
- Edges are edges!

2-D shapes
- Polygons have all straight sides.
- Regular polygons have sides all the same length.
- Parallel lines never meet – think of a train track!
- Perpendicular lines make a right angle.

Triangles
- An isosceles triangle has TWO EQUAL SIDES AND TWO EQUAL ANGLES. Picture an isosceles triangle as an arrow!
- A scalene triangle has THREE SIDES OF DIFFERENT LENGTHS and THREE ANGLES OF DIFFERENT SIZES. When picturing a scalene triangle, think of scaling a mountain that has an easy way up or a more difficult side to climb!
- A right-angled triangle can be isosceles or scalene.

 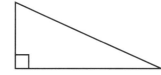

Symmetries
- When drawing reflections, remember to keep the correct distance from the mirror line.
- Remember, rotational symmetry is just working out how many ways the shape can fit EXACTLY on top of itself.

Angles
- Acute angle is between 0° and 89°
- Right angle = 90°
- Obtuse angle is between 91° and 179°
- Straight line = 180°
- Reflex angle is between 181° and 359°

Coordinates
- Always read ALONG the x axis and then UP/DOWN the y axis.
- Always write (x) before (y), i.e. (x, y).

Measuring
Measuring weight and capacity
- 1000 grams = 1 kilogram (1000 g = 1 kg)
- 1000 kilograms = 1 tonne (1000 kg = 1 tonne)
- 1000 millilitres = 1 litre (1000 ml = 1 l)

Estimating measures
- Milli = very small
- Centi = small
- Kilo = big

Perimeter
- Perimeter is the distance all the way round the edge of a flat shape.

Area
- Area is the space covered up by the shape.
- Count the squares and remember area is always measured in square units (cm^2, mm^2, m^2).

Reading scales
- CAREFULLY work out what each mark on the scale is worth.

HANDLING DATA
Pictograms
- With pictograms PICTURE = NUMBER

e.g. ⩙ = 20 ice creams ⸦ = 10 ice creams

Mean, median, range and mode
- Mean = sum of all values divided by number of values
- Median = middle number in sequence (always write down in order first)
- Range = difference between highest and lowest number
- Mode = most common value

Charts and graphs
- Be careful and accurate. Use a sharp pencil.
- Pie charts are good for percentages, fractions or decimals.

USING AND APPLYING MATHEMATICS
Simple formulae
- Talk through the formula in your head. It will make it easier.
Number patterns
- Check the difference between the numbers to find the pattern.

About the National Tests

Key facts

✦ The Key Stage 2 National Tests take place in the summer term in Year 6. You will be tested on Maths and English.

✦ The tests take place in your school and will be marked by examiners – not your teacher!

✦ Individual test scores are not made public but a school's combined scores are published in what are commonly known as 'league tables'.

The Maths National Tests

You will take three tests in Maths:

● **Mental Maths Test** – This test will be played to you on an audio CD. You will have to answer the questions mentally within 5, 10 or 15 seconds. This test will take about 20 minutes.

● **Test A** – The non-calculator test. This test requires quick answers on a test paper. You will not be able to use a calculator but should show any working you do.

● **Test B** – This test allows you to use a calculator and includes problems that will take you longer to solve.

DON'T FORGET!

Using and applying mathematics
There are many questions testing how you use and apply your mathematical knowledge in different situations. This includes:
• knowing which is the important information in the questions
• how to check your results
• describing things mathematically using common symbols and diagrams
• explaining your reasons for conclusions that you make.

Many of the questions include elements of Using and applying mathematics but we have also added extra pages with specific questions designed to help you succeed in this area of maths (pages 53–60).

You might be asked to explain your answers and also write possible answers. Remember, always show your method.

Test techniques

Before the test

1 When you revise, revise little and often rather than in long sessions. Use questions to check you really understand a topic.
2 Learn your multiplication facts and related division facts up to 10 × 10 so that you can recall them quickly.
3 Revise with a friend. You can encourage and learn from each other.
4 Get a good night's sleep the night before.
5 Be prepared – bring your own pens and pencils.

During the test

1 Don't rush the first few questions. These tend to be quite straightforward, so don't make any silly mistakes.
2 As you know by now, READ THE QUESTION THEN READ IT AGAIN.
3 If you get stuck, put a sensible guess and move on. You can come back to it later.
4 Never leave a multiple-choice question. Make an educated guess if you really can't work out the answer.
5 Check how many marks a question is worth. Has your answer 'earned' each mark?
6 Check each answer, perhaps using the inverse or rounding method. Does your answer look correct?
7 Be aware of the time. After 20 minutes, check to see how far you have got.
8 Try to leave a couple of minutes at the end to read through what you have written.
9 Always show your method as this may win a mark even if your answer is wrong.
10 Don't leave any questions unanswered. In the 2 minutes you have left yourself at the end, make an educated guess at the questions you really couldn't do.

Things to remember

1 If you see a difficult question, take your time, re-read it and have a go!
2 Check every question and every page to be sure you don't miss any!
3 If a question is about measuring, always write in the UNIT OF MEASUREMENT.
4 Don't be afraid to ask a teacher for anything you need, such as tracing paper or a protractor.
5 Write neatly – if you want to change an answer, put a line through it and write beside the answer box.
6 Always double-check your answers.

Practise your mental maths skills

Table facts

Practise saying each of your tables. Time how quickly you can say each table. Practise some more and then try to say them faster – how many times can you break your record? Write your record in the chart below. (If you write in pencil you can change your record as you get better!)

Say your tables as division facts as well. Start with:

There is 1 two in 2, there are 2 twos in 4, there are 3 twos in 6 ......

	2x	3x	4x	5x	6x	7x	8x	9x	10x
x									
x									

Number bonds

Ask someone to say numbers to 10 and say the number pair that will make 10. How many can you get right in one minute?

Repeat the game with numbers to 100, saying the number pair that makes 100.

One minute record = _____

Place value

Play a game where someone says a number with the digit 5 in it, like 35 463. You say the value of the digit 5 (this one would be 5000).

How many can you get right in one minute?

One minute record = _____

Fractions, decimals and percentages

Get someone to ask you values like tenths, quarters, halves and thirds. Tell them what they are worth as decimals and percentages. Work as quickly as you can.

One minute record = _____

Number properties

Pick a number between 30 and 50. Write down three multiples, as many factors as you can and state whether it is a prime number. How many numbers can you complete in one minute?

One minute record = _____

Simple formulae

If $6 + d = 20$, what is d worth?

Ask someone to make up sums like these and say them to you. How many can you solve in one minute?

One minute record = _____

Number problems

Make up number problems involving money. You could find prices on the Internet or in catalogues and work out the cost of more than one item, or the change you could get from a larger amount of money than the cost of the item! Challenge a friend to solve your problems.

Angles

1 right angle = _____ °   2 right angles = _____ °

3 right angles = _____ °   4 right angles = _____ °

Use a protractor to get used to angles of other sizes.

Shapes

Polygons have _____   Regular polygons have _____

Faces are   _____   Edges are _____

Vertices are   _____

Ask someone to hold up objects; name the shape and say how many faces, vertices and edges it has. How many objects can you do in one minute?

One minute record = _____

Measures

Milli means   _____

Centi means _____

Kilo means   _____

Get someone to give you measures in km and change them to m, litres to ml, kg to g, cm to mm, m to mm. How many can you do in one minute?

One minute record = _____

Estimating measures

What is the weight of an apple?

What is the length from your hand to your elbow?

What is the capacity of a mug?

Level 3 – The tricky bits

Fractions

Checking your understanding

1 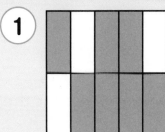 What fraction of the square is shaded?

1 mark

2 Colour $\frac{1}{4}$ of the rectangle.

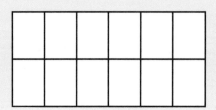

2

1 mark

3 What is $\frac{1}{4}$ of 16?

3

1 mark

4 What fraction of 15 is 5?

4

1 mark

Using and applying

5 Callum and Hannah play a maths game. In the game they have to use the number they throw on a dice to make a fraction.

a) Hannah throws 4 and needs to make a half.

Give two ways she can use the 4 to make a fraction equivalent to a half.

5a

2 marks

b) Callum throws 6 and needs to make a third.

Give two ways he can use the 6 to make a fraction equivalent to a third.

5b

2 marks

6 Leah invites 12 friends to a party. $\frac{1}{4}$ arrive early and $\frac{1}{3}$ arrive late. The rest arrive on time.

How many of her friends come on time?

6

2 marks

Classifying shapes

Checking your understanding

1 Complete these sentences.

a) A cube has ☐ faces. **b)** A sphere has ☐ edges.

c) A cuboid has ☐ vertices. **d)** A triangular prism has ☐ faces.

e) A cone has ☐ edge. **f)** A cylinder has ☐ vertices.

6 marks

2 Look at these shapes.

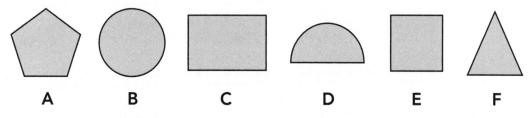

A   B   C   D   E   F

a) Circle the polygons.

b) Put an **R** in the shapes that are regular.

c) Put an **S** in the shapes that have just one line of symmetry.

2a
2 marks

2b
2 marks

2c
2 marks

Using and applying

3 Sort these shapes into three different groups. Label the groups and explain why you grouped them the way you did.

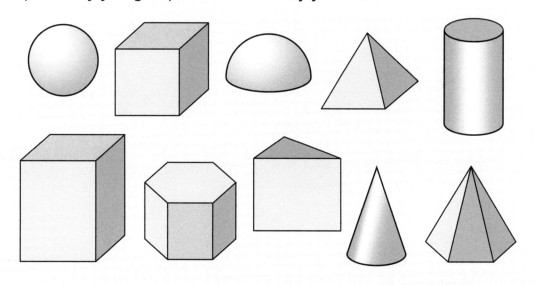

3
2 marks

13

Bar charts and pictograms

1 As part of a project, the Pentagons group had to investigate which countries the children in their class had visited on holiday. They made a bar chart of their results.

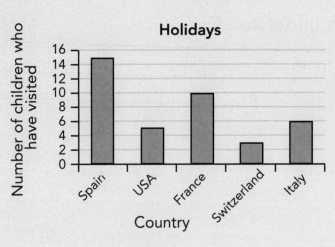

a) How many children had been to the USA?

b) How many more children had visited Spain than Italy?

c) 7 of the children who had visited France went this year. How many visited before this year?

d) Next month, 5 children are going on an exchange trip to Switzerland. Change the graph to show how it will look after the visit.

2 This pictogram shows the number of matches different school teams won last year.

Netball	
Football	
Kwik cricket	
Cross country	
Short tennis	

 = 4 wins

a) The Kwik cricket team won 14 matches. Show this on the pictogram.

b) How many more wins did the football team have than the cross country team?

c) Miguel plays on the short tennis and the netball teams. How many wins did he have last year?

d) How many wins did the school have altogether?

Decimal notation and negative numbers

Checking your understanding

1 Write these amounts as decimal numbers.

a) 5 pounds and 35 pence

= £ [ ]

b) 3 pounds and 68 pence

= £ [ ]

c) 10 pounds and 21 pence

= £ [ ]

d) 8 pounds and 50 pence

= £ [ ]

e) 4 pounds and 3 pence

= £ [ ]

f) 5 pounds and 7 pence

= £ [ ]

[ ] 1

6 marks

2 Put the missing numbers on each mark on this thermometer.

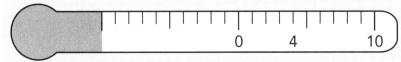

0   4   10

[ ] 2

1 mark

3 Circle the amount that is greater in each pair.

a) £4.50   or   £4.05

b) £5.70   or   £5.09

[ ] 3

2 marks

Using and applying

4 Write the value of:

a) 30 ten pences as a decimal number [ ]

[ ] 4a

1 mark

b) 7 fifty pences as a decimal number [ ]

[ ] 4b

1 mark

5 The diver is climbing the ladder in and out of the water.

a) If the diver starts on the −4 step and climbs up 6 steps, which step will he be on?

[ ]

b) If the diver climbs down 5 steps and ends on step −1, on which step did he start?

[ ]

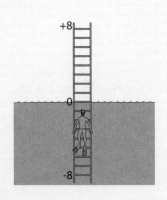

+8

0

-8

[ ] 5a

1 mark

[ ] 5b

1 mark

15

Place value

Check your understanding

1 Write the value of the digit 5 in each of these numbers.

a) 657 ☐   b) 523 ☐   c) 5137 ☐

2 marks 1

2 How many tens do you need to make 340? ☐

1 mark 2

3 Write these numbers in order of size, starting with the smallest.

705   755   507   577   570   750

☐ ☐ ☐ ☐ ☐ ☐

1 mark 3

4 Circle the number that is closest to 380.

372   383   281   378   279

1 mark 4

5 Circle the numbers that are 150 when rounded to the nearest 10.

147   156   145   143   155

1 mark 5

6 Write these amounts of money in order, starting with the smallest.

99p   £2.35   £0.65   £8   25p   £2

☐ ☐ ☐ ☐ ☐ ☐

1 mark 6

7 How many 10p coins do you need to make £24.50? ☐

1 mark 7

8 Write these numbers in order of size, starting with the smallest.

0.534   0.753   0.347   0.75   0.7   0.374

☐ ☐ ☐ ☐ ☐ ☐

1 mark 8

9 Round these numbers to the nearest whole number.

a) 82.8 ☐   b) 4.39 ☐   c) 12.5 ☐

2 marks 9

10 Write the next three numbers in each of these sequences.

a) 4.12, 4.14, 4.16, ☐ , ☐ , ☐

b) 0.01, 0.02, 0.03, ☐ , ☐ , ☐

c) 1.1, 1.5, 1.9, ☐ , ☐ , ☐

☐ 10

2 marks

Using and applying

11 Sam has a set of four number cards. Write the number that is three hundred more than the largest number he can make with the cards.

4 8 3 5

☐

☐ 11

1 mark

12 Write the number the arrow is pointing at on this number line.

100 ⬇ 200

☐

☐ 12

1 mark

13 Safi rounds the number of kilometres she has travelled in one week to the nearest 10 and says she has travelled 240 km. What are the greatest and least number of kilometres she could have travelled?

Greatest = ☐   Least = ☐

☐ 13

2 marks

14 Four children ran a race. Their finishing times were:

Name	James	Emma	Billy	Talib
Time (in seconds)	23.6	19.8	23.4	25.7

a) Who won the race? ☐

☐ 14a

1 mark

b) What was the difference in time between Billy and James? ☐

☐ 14b

1 mark

15 Michelle jumped 1.32 m in the standing long jump.
Dan jumped five tenths of a metre further.

How far did Dan jump? ☐

☐ 15

1 mark

Total marks for this topic ☐

17

Multiplying by 10 and 100

Checking your understanding

1 Fill in the missing numbers.

a) 34 × 100 = [   ]   b) [   ] × 100 = 35,000

c) 48,000 ÷ [   ] = 480   d) [   ] ÷ 10 = 720

[   ] 1

2 marks

2 Complete these calculations.

a) 27 × (36 + 64) = [   ]   b) (35 + 25) × 100 = [   ]

[   ] 2

2 marks

Using and applying

3 Work out an approximate answer to these calculations by rounding the numbers.

a) 398 × 9 = [   ] × [   ] = [   ]

[   ] 3a

1 mark

b) 34 × 103 = [   ] × [   ] = [   ]

[   ] 3b

1 mark

4 James has 47 stickers in his collection. Caitlin has 10 times as many.

How many stickers does Caitlin have? [   ]

[   ] 4

1 mark

5 Billy has run 100 metres every day for 5 weeks.

How many metres has he run altogether? [   ]

[   ] 5

1 mark

6 Aadi collects 100 pennies each from 58 different people.

How many pennies has he collected? [   ]

[   ] 6

1 mark

7 Talib says that 20 × 100 is 20,000.

Is he right?   YES   NO

Explain why. [   ]

[   ] 7

1 mark

Total marks for this topic   [   ]

18

MATHEMATICS

Answers for
Practice Questions

Page 12

1 $\frac{7}{10}$

2 E.g.  Any three pieces coloured.

3 4

4 $\frac{1}{3}$ (or equivalent fraction)

5 a) $\frac{2}{4}$, $\frac{4}{8}$ (1 mark each)
   b) $\frac{2}{6}$, $\frac{6}{18}$ (1 mark each)

6 5 (2 marks; 1 mark for incorrect answer but evidence of correct working)

Page 13

1 a) 6   b) 0   c) 8
   d) 5   e) 1   f) 0

2 a) A, C, E and F circled (2 marks; 1 mark for 2 or 3 marked correctly)
   b) A and E (1 mark each; deduct 1 mark for each shape marked incorrectly)
   c) D and F (1 mark each; deduct 1 mark for each shape marked incorrectly)

3 1 mark for sorting into groups matching chosen criteria; 1 mark for coherent explanation

Page 14

1 a) 5   b) 9   c) 3
   d) Switzerland bar extended to 8

2 a) $3\frac{1}{2}$ medals drawn
   b) 9   c) 20   d) 45

Page 15

1 a) £5.35   b) £3.68   c) £10.21
   d) £8.50   e) £4.03   f) £5.07

2 -10-9-8-7-6-5-4-3-2-1 0 1 2 3 4 5 6 7 8 9 10

3 a) £4.50   b) £5.70
4 a) £3.00   b) £3.50
5 a) 2   b) 4

Pages 16–17

1 a) 50
   b) 500
   c) 5000 (2 marks for all correct, 1 mark for 2 correct)

2 34

3 507, 570, 577, 705, 750, 755

4 378

5 147 and 145 **both** circled

6 25p, £0.65, 99p, £2, £2.35, £8

7 245

8 0.347, 0.374, 0.534, 0.7, 0.75, 0.753

9 a) 83   b) 4   c) 13   (1 mark for 2 correct, 2 marks for all correct)

10 a) 4.18, 4.20/4.2, 4.22
    b) 0.04, 0.05, 0.06
    c) 2.3, 2.7, 3.1
    (1 mark for 2 sequences correct, 2 marks for all correct)

11 8843

12 Answers in the range 165–175 inclusive

13 greatest = 244 km (1 mark); least = 235 (1 mark)

14 a) Emma
    b) 0.2 seconds (or 2/10 seconds)

15 1.82 m

Page 18

1 a) 3400   b) 350
   c) 100   d) 7200
   (2 marks for all correct; 1 mark for 2 or more correct)

2 a) 2700   b) 6000

3 a) 400 × 10 = 4000
   b) 30 × 100 = 3000

4 470

5 3500 m (or 3.5 km or $3\frac{1}{2}$ km)

6 5800

7 No. Multiplying 20 by 100 pushes the 20 two places to the left, leaving two places for zeros, making 2000.

Page 19

1 a) 10   b) 230
   c) 10   d) 380
   (2 marks for all correct; 1 mark for 2 or more correct)

2 a) 2   b) 40

3 a) 800 ÷ 100 = 8
   b) 500 ÷ 10 = 50

4 14

5 56,400p

6 30 days

7 670 m

8 No. Dividing 530,000 by 1000 pushes the 530,000 three places to the right, removing three zeros and making 530.

Page 20

1 3940

2 930

3 a) 267   b) 369

4 179

5 37 + 38

6 £461

7 £68 (2 marks for correct answer; 1 mark for evidence of correct working but incorrect answer)

Page 21

1 119

2 3737

3 72 and 34 both circled

4 a) 188   b) 611

5 157

6 £14

7 69

8 31 (2 marks for correct answer; 1 mark for evidence of correct working but incorrect answer)

9 £63

Page 22

1 a) 210   b) 608   c) 215   d) 558

2 a) 8   b) 54   c) 7   d) 85

3 a) >   b) >   c) <

4 1 × 100 or 2 × 50 or 4 × 25 or 5 × 20 or 10 × 10

5 a) 120   b) 165
   (2 marks each for correct answer, 1 mark for incorrect answer but evidence of correct working)

Page 23

1 a) 19   b) 18   c) 129   d) 14

2 a) 201   b) 4   c) 6   d) 301

3
    220 ÷ 4   84 ÷ 3 + 26

    2 × 108 ÷ 4   224 ÷ 4

    110 × 5 ÷ 10   140 ÷ 5 + 28

   (2 marks for all correct, 1 mark for 2 correct)

4 a) £22   b) £26   c) 17 days

Page 24

1 a) 11.1   b) 15   c) 2.9   d) 2.6

2 a) 19.7   b) 18.6

c) 39.85   d) 67.31

3 a) 16.80   b) 94.95
   c) 18.69   d) 37.86

4 <150 = d   >150 = a, b   = 150 = c
   (2 marks for all correct, 1 mark for 2 or 3 correct)

5 1.5 km

Page 25

1 a) 1:3 or 1 to every 3
   b) $\frac{1}{4}$ or 1 in every 4

2 a) 1:5 or 1 to every 5
   b) $\frac{5}{6}$ or 5 in every 6

3 a) 1:2 or 1 to every 2
   b) $\frac{4}{9}$ or 4 in every 9
   c) 1:2 or 1 to every 2
   d) $\frac{1}{9}$ or 1 in every 9

Pages 26–27

1 a) 350 + 400 = 750
   b) 570 – 240 = 330
   c) 60 × 10 = 600
   d) 750 ÷ 10 = 75

2 a) even   b) odd   c) even
   d) even   e) odd   f) even
   (2 correct for 1 mark, max 3 marks)

3 a) 356 + 134 = 490   490 – 356 = 134
      490 – 134 = 356   (all for 1 mark)
   b) 4 × 451 = 1804   1804 ÷ 4 = 451
      1804 ÷ 451 = 4   (all for 1 mark)
   c) 472 ÷ 59 = 8   59 × 8 = 472
      8 × 59 = 472   (all for 1 mark)

4 YES – 567 is an odd number and 368 is an even number. If you add an odd number and an even number you get an odd number.
   OR: 8 + 7 in the units is 15, so the answer will end in 5 and be an odd number.
   (up to 3 marks, depending on the clarity of the answer)

5 Multiplying a one-digit number by a two-digit number can't give a four-digit number.
   OR: 99 is the biggest two-digit number and 99 × 10 = 990, which is not a four-digit number (or similar).
   OR: He knows 4 × 25 = 100 and his answer is a lot bigger than that.
   (up to 3 marks, depending on the clarity of the answer)

6 Add from the top to the bottom and then the bottom to the top.
   OR: Add the numbers in a different order.
   OR: Round the numbers and add them.
   (NOT do the calculation again – this option is removed in the question).
   Michelle's answer is wrong. The correct answer is 840.
   (up to 2 marks per method, depending on the clarity of the answer)

Page 28

1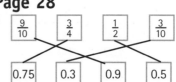
   (2 marks for all correct, 1 mark for 2 correct)

2 0.333333...

3 $\frac{4}{10}$ or $\frac{2}{5}$ or equivalent; 0.4 (1 mark each)

4 a) 9 pieces coloured
   b) $\frac{1}{10}$ and 0.1 (1 mark each)

5 none

Page 29

1. **a)** $\frac{1}{2}$ or 50% or 0.5
   b) $\frac{1}{4}$ or 25% or 0.25
   c) $\frac{2}{11}$ or 18% or 0.18
   d) $\frac{2}{3}$ or 66% or 0.6 or 0.66
   e) $\frac{1}{3}$ or 33% or 0.3 or 0.33
2. cells completed correctly
   1 mark for each cell correct to a maximum of 12 marks

Fraction	Decimal	Percentage
	1.0	100%
$\frac{1}{2}$ or equivalent		50%
	0.1	10%
$\frac{1}{4}$ or equivalent	0.25	
$\frac{1}{100}$ or equivalent	0.01	
$\frac{3}{4}$ or equivalent		75%

Page 30

1. 1, 2, 3, 6, 9, 18
   (2 marks for all factors, 1 mark for 4 or 5 factors and no more than 1 incorrect)
2. 25
3. 7, 14, 21
4. **a)** 402
   b) The digits of the number add up to make a multiple of 3.
5. **a)** 9
   b) It is made by a 3 × 3 grid, which is square.
6.

	Multiples of 4	Not multiples of 4
Factors of 12	4, 12	1, 2, 3, 6
Not factors of 12	8	5, 7, 9, 10, 11

(2 marks for all correct; 1 mark for at least 8 numbers correctly placed)

Page 31

1. **a)** 13 cm   **b)** 23 cm
   c) 71 cm   **d)** 119 cm
2. The number of weeks multiplied by 7.
3. The number of boxes multiplied by 6.
4. The length of one side multiplied by 4.
5. The number of days multiplied by 24.

Pages 32–33

1. **a)** A (5, 8), B (8, 3), C (4, 0), D (1, 4), E (1, 1), F (2, 6) *(1 mark each)*
   b)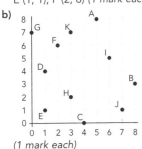
   (1 mark each)
2. **a)** Line from C ending at (4, 5)
   b) (4, 5) *(1 mark for each coordinate)*
3. **a)** (2, 8) OR one of: (5, 0), (5, 1), (5, 3), (5, 4), (5, 5), (5, 6), (5, 7) (5, 8)
   b) (2, 2)
4. (1, 1), (5, 1) and (5, 7) OR (1, 3), (7, 3) and (7, 7)
   (2 marks for all correct, 1 mark for 2 correct)
5. **a)** (2, 5)
   b) (3, 3) marked as D

Page 34

1. **a)** Equilateral; all sides and angles marked as equal
   b) Scalene; no sides or angles marked as equal
   c) Isosceles; 2 sides and 2 angles marked as equal
   (2 marks per triangle)
2. **a)** Triangles C and E marked with a cross
   b) Right angle marked in every triangle *(1 mark)*
3. side 2 = 6 cm   side 3 = 6 cm
   total of all sides = 18 cm *(3 marks, 1 mark each)*
4. One side as 10 cm and the other **not** 10 cm
   OR other 2 sides equal but **not** 10 cm
   (2 marks, 1 mark each)

Page 35

1. **a)** 12   **b)** 8
2. Four from:
   Two pairs of equal sides/opposite sides are equal
   4 sides
   4 right angles
   Two pairs of parallel lines
   Two pairs of perpendicular lines
   (4 marks, 1 for each property identified)
3.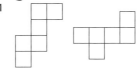
   (3 marks for all correct, 2 marks for 5 or more markings correct, 1 mark for 3 or more markings correct; deduct 1 mark for each incorrect marking)
4. Lines drawn parallel *(1 mark)*; lines 3 cm apart *(1 mark)*

Pages 36–37

1.
   These nets ticked *(1 mark each, deduct 1 mark for each incorrect answer)*
2. 2 triangles and 3 rectangles ticked
3. Sphere and cylinder *(1 mark each, deduct 1 mark for each incorrect answer)*
4. 6 faces, 8 vertices and 12 edges *(1 mark each)*
5. 5 rectangles and 1 hexagon drawn *(1 mark)*, Correctly positioned for a net *(1 mark)*
6. **a)**
   b)
7. **a)** 25   **b)** 30
8. **a)** 9   **b)** 22

Page 38

1. Angles B and D circled *(1 mark each, deduct 1 mark for each incorrect answer)*
2. B and C circled, A and E crossed out *(3 marks for all correct, 2 marks for 3 correct and 1 mark for 2 correct; deduct 1 mark for each incorrect angle)*
3. D, B, E, A, C

4a) and 4b): *(2 marks each for correct answer, 1 mark for evidence of correct working but incorrect answer)*
4. **a)** 35°   **b)** 59°

Page 39

1. 120 cm
2. **a)** 4 cm
   b) 20 cm
3. Rectangle drawn 8 cm by 5 cm *(1 mark for correct length, 1 mark for correct breadth, 1 mark for straight lines accurately drawn)*

Pages 40–41

1.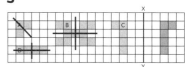
   a) Lines as shown *(1 mark for each correct line, deduct 1 mark for each incorrect line)*
   b) Reflection as shown above *(2 marks correct, 1 mark for right shape in wrong position)*
2.
   (2 marks for each correct tile; 1 mark per tile if at least 3 squares shaded correctly)
3.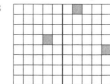
   (1 mark for each square correctly shaded; deduct 1 mark for each square incorrectly shaded)
4.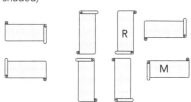
   (1 mark for each letter)
5.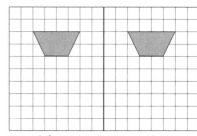
   (1 mark for each vertex correctly positioned)

Page 42

1. 20 cm
2. 32 cm
3. **a)** E   **b)** B and D
4. 24 cm
5 and **6**: *(2 marks each for correct answer, 1 mark for evidence of correct working but incorrect answer)*
5. 5 cm
6. 4 cm

Page 43

1 **a)** 9 cm²
   b) 18 cm² *(2 marks each for correct answer, 1 mark for evidence of correct working but incorrect answer)*
   c) 12 cm²
2a) to **2c):** *(2 marks each for correct answer, 1 mark for evidence of correct working but incorrect answer)*
2 **a)** 8 cm²   **b)** 15 cm²   **c)** 20 cm²
3 6 m²
4 40 m²

Page 44

1 86 mm
2

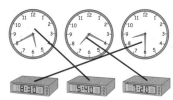

(2 marks for all correct, 1 mark for 2 correct)

3 **a)** 5000 g   **b)** 3000 ml   **c)** 200 mm
   d) 50 m   **e)** 8000 mm   **f)** ½ or 0.5 kg
   (1 mark for every 3 correct answers – maximum 2 marks)
4 **a)** Fact Finders
   b) 1 hour and 55 minutes *(2 marks for correct answer, 1 mark for incorrect answer but evidence of correct working)*
   c) 15 minutes
   d) Top Marks

Page 45

1 **a)** A = 20, B = 45, C = 7–9 inclusive *(2 marks for all correct, 1 mark for 2 correct)*
   b) arrow between 30 and 33 inclusive
2 **a)** D = 140, E = 190, F = 121–125 inclusive *(2 marks for all correct, 1 mark for 2 correct)*
   b) arrow between 152 and 158 inclusive
3 **a)** 70 ml
   b) 1600 ml or 1.6 litres or 1 litre 600 ml
   c) 3.5 litres or 3500 ml or 3 litres 500 ml
4

```
1800          1900          ↓          2000
├─────────────┼─────────────┼─────────────┤
```

Pages 46–47

1 **a)** 4:20 or 20 past 4
   b) 3:30 or ½ past 3
   c) 5:58 or 2 minutes to 6
   d) 9:10 or 10 past 9
2 **a)** 3:40 or 20 to 4
   b) 6:15 or ¼ past 6
   c) 10:55 or 5 to 11
   d) 12:05 or 5 past 12
3 **a)** 8:16 or 16 past 8
   b) 17 minutes
   c) 31 minutes
   d) 25 minutes
   e) in the last column 9:50, 9:56, 10:04, 10:21 *(1 mark for each except 9:50)*
4 **a)** ¼ past 8 or 8:15
   b) i) 2 a.m.
      ii) It is the middle of the night in London – her sister will be in bed!

Pages 48–49

1 **a)** 16–18 (inclusive)
   b) 1:30 p.m. and 5:30 p.m. (+/− 10 minutes)

---

   c) 3 p.m. and 6 p.m.
   d) 16
   e) There are children there in the afternoon, so it can't be a school day. *(2 marks)*
2 **a)**

(award up to 3 marks)
   b) Tuesday and Wednesday
   c) That's when he learnt the most tricks.
3 **a)** August   **b)** March and October
   c) 18°C (+/− 1)
   d) It increased till May, then fell in June, rose till August and then decreased quite sharply through to December. *(2 marks for comprehensive description; 1 mark for creditable attempt)*

Pages 50–51

1 **a)** Check graphs drawn and award up to 4 marks for neatness and accuracy. Groups should have a range of about 5, in which case 0–4 is the most common for **1b**.
2 **a)** India
   b) 26–27 minutes (inclusive)
   c) 12–13 minutes *(2 marks)*
   d) 392 minutes (+/− 10 minutes) *(2 marks)*
   e) Check graphs drawn and award up to 4 marks for neatness and accuracy. Groups should have a range of about 5, in which case 10–15 is most common for **2f**.

Page 52

1 **a)** range = 2   mode = 4
   b) range = 2.2   mode = 8.4
   c) range = 288   mode = 612
2 **a)** No, because the largest number was 65 and the smallest was 41; 65 − 41 = 24, so the range is 24. *(2 marks for correct answer, 1 mark for partial answer)*
   b) 53 minutes

Page 53

1 **a)** 11, 14, 17   Rule: add 3 *(2 marks)*
   b) 5, 3, 1   Rule: subtract 2 *(2 marks)*
2 **a)** 5, 9, 13, 17, 21   **b)** 20, 14, 8, 2, −4
   c) 1, 4, 10, 22, 46
3 **a)** 11, 7   **b)** 13, 19   **c)** 16, 27

Pages 54–56

1 **a)** £26.49   **b)** £7.02
2 3.64 kg
3 **a)** 2.8 litres   **b)** 1.4 litres
4 It costs £6.50 to get to Whitehall. A climbing session costs £9.80. *(1 mark each, deduct 1 mark for each statement ticked incorrectly)*
5 and 6: *(2 marks each for correct answer, 1 mark for evidence of correct working but incorrect answer)*
5 £13.80 (NOT £13.8)
6 294p or £2.94
7 66 × 2 = 132 or 22 × 6 = 132
8 £112 *(2 marks for correct answer, 1 mark for incorrect answer but evidence of correct working)*

---

9 **a)** Cross out 'She gets £1.50 pocket money a week. She reads the magazine over 3 days.'
   b) 594p or £5.94 *(2 marks for correct answer, 1 mark for incorrect answer but evidence of correct working)*
10a) and **10b):** *(2 marks each for correct answer, 1 mark for evidence of correct working but incorrect answer)*
10 **a)** 392 kilometres
    b) 399 minutes or 6 hours and 39 minutes
11 19
12 50
13 **a)** 17   **b)** 13   **c)** 26

Page 57

1 and 2a): *(2 marks each for correct answer, 1 mark for evidence of correct working but incorrect answer)*
1 **a)** 1.37 p.m.   **b)** 13
2 **a)** 50
   b) 1.2 kg or 1200 g
3 **a)** 8.49 km   **b)** 3.19 km   **c)** 7.95 km

Page 58

1 **a)**

   b) pentagon   **c)** 1
2 Example:

   *(Make sure there are only **two** pairs of perpendicular lines.)*
3 semi-circle (or crescent)
4 **a)** 20 cm   **b)** 10 cm   **c)** 60 cm

Page 59

1 **a)** 27.08 m
   b) 3.99 m between years 3 and 4 *(2 marks for correct answer, 1 mark for incorrect answer but evidence of correct working)*
   c) Year 3
2 **a)** Tuesday 30, Thursday 46–48 inclusive *(1 mark each)*
   b) Wednesday
   c) Because just a few books were taken out.
   d) 9 whole books drawn and about ⅓ of a book

Page 60

1 Because 8 × 30p is 240p which is £2.40
2 **a)** Isaac
   b) 6 × 50 km = 300 km so that's 6 hours
3 **a)** No   **b)** 6
   c) 10 × 6 = 60 minutes and 60 minutes = 1 hour

Dividing by 10 and 100

Checking your understanding

1 Fill in the missing numbers.

a) 75 × ☐ = 750

b) 23,000 ÷ 100 = ☐

c) 6700 ÷ ☐ = 670

d) 3800 ÷ 10 = ☐

☐ 1

2 marks

2 Complete these calculations.

a) (4 × 5) ÷ 10 = ☐

b) 400 ÷ (15 − 5) = ☐

☐ 2

2 marks

Using and applying

3 Work out an approximate answer to these calculations by rounding the numbers.

a) 765 ÷ 107 = ☐ ÷ ☐ = ☐

☐ 3a

1 mark

b) 502 ÷ 8.9 = ☐ ÷ ☐ = ☐

☐ 3b

1 mark

4 Aunty Anne gives each of her nephews and nieces £100. If it costs her £1400, how many nephews and nieces does she have?

☐

☐ 4

1 mark

5 How many pennies in £564? ☐

☐ 5

1 mark

6 Kevin has to read a book with 300 pages. If he reads 10 pages a day, how long will it take him to read it? ☐

☐ 6

1 mark

7 How many metres can you make with 67,000 cm? ☐

☐ 7

1 mark

8 Ben says that 530,000 ÷ 1000 is 5300.
Is he right?   YES   NO

☐ 8

Explain why. ☐

1 mark

Total marks for this topic ☐

19

Addition

Checking your understanding

1 258 + 3586 + 96 =

1 mark 1

2 What is the sum of 356 and 574?

1 mark 2

3 Fill in the missing numbers.

a) 46 + ☐ = 313   b) ☐ + 271 = 640

2 marks 3

Using and applying

4 Grumps complained about 47 things on Monday, 74 things on Tuesday and 58 things on Wednesday. How many things had he complained about altogether?

1 mark 4

5 Use each of these number cards once to complete the sum.

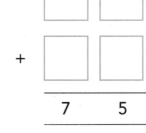

1 mark 5

6 Billy buys a new computer. The computer costs £369. Delivery costs £24. He upgrades the memory at a cost of £68. What is the total cost?

1 mark 6

7 Gary saves £12. Neville saves double the amount that Gary saves and Louise saves £8 more than Neville. How much did they save altogether?

2 marks 7

Total marks for this topic

Subtraction

Checking your understanding

1 406 – 287 = ☐

2 4005 – 268 = ☐

3 Circle the numbers that have a difference of 38.

46   72   90   18   34   40

4 Fill in the missing numbers.

a) 673 – ☐ = 485   b) ☐ – 243 = 368

Using and applying

5 Ben collects 246 football stickers. He gives 89 to his brother. How many stickers does he have left?

☐

6 Yin Wai buys some jeans and a jacket. The total cost is £62. If the jacket cost £48, how much did the jeans cost?

☐

7 Sam has 157 pages left to read in his book. Harry has 88. How many more pages has Sam got to read than Harry?

☐

8 There are 45 children in the playground at 4 p.m. By 4:30, 26 children have gone home and 12 more have arrived. How many children are in the playground now?

☐

9 Dan goes shopping in the sale. He buys some football boots for £37. How much money will he have left if he had £100 to start with?

☐

1 mark   **1**

1 mark   **2**

1 mark   **3**

1 mark   **4**

1 mark   **5**

1 mark   **6**

1 mark   **7**

2 marks   **8**

1 mark   **9**

Total marks for this topic ☐

Short multiplication

Checking your understanding

1 **a)** 35 × 6 = ☐   **b)** 76 × 8 = ☐

   c) 43 × 5 = ☐   **d)** 62 × 9 = ☐

☐ 1

4 marks

2 Fill in the missing numbers.

   a) 35 × ☐ = 280   **b)** ☐ × 9 = 486

   c) ☐ × 26 = 182   **d)** 7 × ☐ = 595

☐ 2

4 marks

3 Write <, >, or = in these equations (remember to multiply before you add!).

   a) 53 × 5 ☐ 110 × 2 + 25

☐ 3a

1 mark

   b) 675 – 245 ☐ 65 × 4 + 150

☐ 3b

1 mark

   c) 6 × 24 + 31 ☐ 25 × 9 + 115

☐ 3c

1 mark

4 Give two numbers that have a product of 100. ☐ ☐

☐ 4

1 mark

Using and applying

5 Work through these number problems.

   a) Start with 16. Multiply by 4, subtract 4 and double the answer.

☐ 5a

2 marks

   b) Start with 21. Multiply by 5, add 5, halve and multiply by 3.

☐ 5b

2 marks

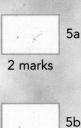

Short division

Checking your understanding

1 Calculate:

a) $76 \div 4 =$ [ ]

b) $54 \div 3 =$ [ ]

c) $645 \div 5 =$ [ ]

d) $98 \div 7 =$ [ ]

[ ] 1

4 marks

2 Fill in the missing numbers.

a) [ ] $\div 3 = 67$

b) $464 \div$ [ ] $= 116$

c) $582 \div$ [ ] $= 97$

d) [ ] $\div 7 = 43$

[ ] 2

4 marks

3 Join the calculations that have the same answers. You must multiply and divide before you add!

$220 \div 4$ $84 \div 3 + 26$

$2 \times 108 \div 4$ $224 \div 4$

$110 \times 5 \div 10$ $140 \div 5 + 28$

[ ] 3

2 marks

Using and applying

4 Whitney spent £154 on a week's holiday. She spent the same amount each day.

a) How much did Whitney spend each day?

 4a

1 mark

b) Her twin, Tegan, spent £182 on the same holiday. How much did Tegan spend each day?

[ ] 4b

1 mark

c) Tegan decides she needs £8 a day for food when she goes away in the summer. If she has £136 saved for food, how many days can she stay away?

[ ] 4c

1 mark

Total marks for this topic [ ]

Adding and subtracting decimals

Checking your understanding

1 Write the answers to these calculations, using your knowledge of adding and subtracting two-digit numbers.

a) $4.5 + 6.6 =$ [   ]

b) $7.5 + 7.5 =$ [   ]

c) $8.2 - 5.3 =$ [   ]

d) $5.1 - 2.5 =$ [   ]

[   ] 1

4 marks

2 Calculate:

a) $12.8 + 6.9 =$ [   ]

b) $26.4 - 7.8 =$ [   ]

c) $56.64 - 16.79 =$ [   ]

d) $39.46 + 27.85 =$ [   ]

[   ] 2

4 marks

3 Fill in the missing numbers.

a) $36.20 -$ [   ] $= 19.40$

b) [   ] $- 73.27 = 21.68$

c) $78.54 +$ [   ] $= 97.23$

d) [   ] $+ 47.45 = 85.31$

[   ] 3

4 marks

4 Write the letters next to the calculations in the correct boxes.

a) $136.5 + 82.7 - 63.4$

b) $13.4 + 148.8 - 11.2$

c) $27.97 + 86.48 + 35.55$

d) $93.57 - 35.63 + 91.08$

<150	>150	=150

[   ] 4

2 marks

Using and applying

5 It is 4.3 km from Joe's house to the football pitch. He ran 2.8 km and walked the rest of the way. How far did he walk?

[   ]

[   ] 5

1 mark

Total marks for this topic [   ]

Ratio and proportion

Checking your understanding

For all the questions, write your answers in the simplest form!

1

    a) The ratio of white to blue phones = [　　　]

 1a

1 mark

    b) The proportion of white phones = [　　　]

[　　] 1b

1 mark

2

    a) The ratio of buses to cars = [　　　]

[　　] 2a

1 mark

    b) The proportion of cars = [　　　]

[　　] 2b

1 mark

3

[　　] 3a

1 mark

    a) The ratio of large stars to small stars = [　　　]

[　　] 3b

1 mark

    b) The proportion of small blue stars = [　　　]

[　　] 3c

1 mark

    c) The ratio of white stars to blue stars = [　　　]

[　　] 3d

1 mark

    d) The proportion of large white stars = [　　　]

Total marks for this topic [　　]

25

Checking your answers

Checking your understanding

1 Use rounding to give an approximate answer to these calculations.

a) 354 + 398

1a

1 mark

b) 574 − 235

1b

1 mark

c) 57 × 8

1c

1 mark

d) 753 ÷ 9

1d

1 mark

2 Fill the blanks with 'odd' or 'even'.

a) If you add or subtract two even numbers you get an

number.

b) If you add or subtract an odd and an even number you get an

number.

c) If you add or subtract two odd numbers you get an

number.

d) If you multiply or divide two even numbers you get an

number.

e) If you multiply or divide two odd numbers you get an

number.

f) If you multiply or divide an odd and an even number you get an

number.

2

3 marks

3 Write three other calculations you could make from each.

a) 134 + 356 = 490 [ ] [ ] [ ]

b) 451 × 4 = 1804 [ ] [ ] [ ]

c) 472 ÷ 8 = 59 [ ] [ ] [ ]

Using and applying

4 James says

> If I add 567 and 368, I know the answer will be an odd number.

Is he correct?   YES   NO

Explain your answer.

[ ]

5 Ben multiplies 6 by 28 and gets the answer 1248. He looks at his answer and knows immediately that it is wrong. Explain how he knows by looking at it that it is wrong.

[ ]

6 Michelle does this sum:

```
   4 6 8
       9
     8 6
 + 2 7 7
```

She gets the answer 830. Explain two ways she could do the calculation differently to check her answer.

a) [ ]

b) [ ]

Total marks for this topic [ ]

Proportions of a whole

Checking your understanding

1 Match these fractions with the decimal that is worth the same.

| $\frac{9}{10}$ | $\frac{3}{4}$ | $\frac{1}{2}$ | $\frac{3}{10}$ |

| 0.75 | 0.3 | 0.9 | 0.5 |

1
2 marks

2 Write the decimal that is the same as $\frac{1}{3}$. [ ]

2
1 mark

3 What fraction of this shape is shaded?

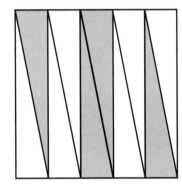

Write your answer as a fraction and as a decimal.

[ ] and [ ]

3
2 marks

Using and applying

4 Cyla eats 0.5 of a cake and Ben eats $\frac{4}{10}$.

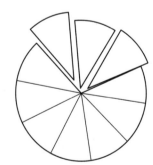

a) Shade the cake to show how much they have eaten together.

b) Write as a decimal and as a fraction how much cake is left.

4a
1 mark

4b
2 marks

5 Kate sweeps 0.25 of the playground and James sweeps $\frac{3}{4}$.

How much of the playground still has to be swept?

5
1 mark

Total marks for this topic [ ]

28

Important proportions

Checking your understanding

For all the questions, write your answers in the simplest form!

1 Approximately what proportion of the shapes in each box is square?

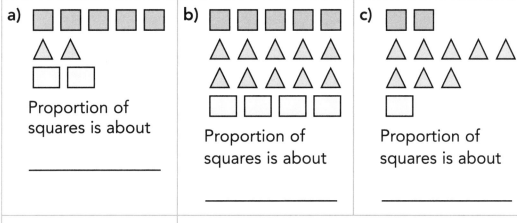

a) Proportion of squares is about

_____

b) Proportion of squares is about

_____

c) Proportion of squares is about

_____

d) Proportion of squares is about

_____

e) Proportion of squares is about

_____

1

5 marks

2 Complete the table.

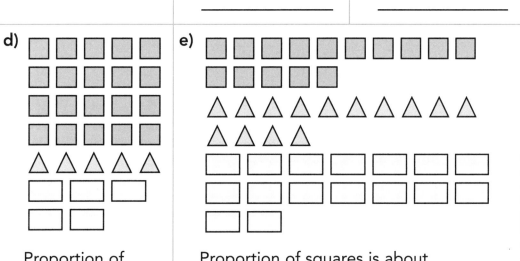

Fraction	Decimal	Percentage
$\frac{1}{1}$ = 1 whole		
	0.5	
$\frac{1}{10}$		
		25%
		1%
	0.75	

2

12 marks

Total marks for this topic [ ]

29

Number relationships

Checking your understanding

1 List the factors of 18.

[ ] 1

2 marks

2 What is 5 squared?

[ ] 2

1 mark

3 Write the first three multiples of 7.

[ ] 3

1 mark

Using and applying

4 a) Write the first multiple of 3 greater than 400.

[ ] 4a

1 mark

b) Explain how you know which numbers are multiples of 3.

[ ] 4b

1 mark

5 a) Circle the square number: 5   6   7   8   9   10

[ ] 5a

1 mark

b) Explain why it is a square number.

[ ] 5b

1 mark

6 Sort these numbers into the Carroll diagram:
1, 2, 3, 4, 5, 6, 7, 8, 9, 10, 11, 12

	Multiples of 4	Not multiples of 4
Factors of 12		
Not factors of 12		

[ ] 6

2 marks

Total marks for this topic

[ ]

MATHEMATICS

Answers for
Practice Questions

Page 12

1 $\frac{7}{10}$

2 E.g. 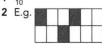 Any three pieces coloured.

3 4

4 $\frac{1}{3}$ (or equivalent fraction)

5 a) $\frac{2}{4}$, $\frac{4}{8}$ (1 mark each)
   b) $\frac{2}{6}$, $\frac{6}{18}$ (1 mark each)

6 5 (2 marks; 1 mark for incorrect answer but evidence of correct working)

Page 13

1 a) 6   b) 0   c) 8
   d) 5   e) 1   f) 0

2 a) A, C, E and F circled (2 marks; 1 mark for 2 or 3 marked correctly)
   b) A and E (1 mark each; deduct 1 mark for each shape marked incorrectly)
   c) D and F (1 mark each; deduct 1 mark for each shape marked incorrectly)

3 1 mark for sorting into groups matching chosen criteria; 1 mark for coherent explanation

Page 14

1 a) 5   b) 9   c) 3
   d) Switzerland bar extended to 8

2 a) $3\frac{1}{2}$ medals drawn
   b) 9   c) 20   d) 45

Page 15

1 a) £5.35   b) £3.68   c) £10.21
   d) £8.50   e) £4.03   f) £5.07

2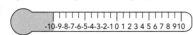
   -10-9-8-7-6-5-4-3-2-1 0 1 2 3 4 5 6 7 8 9 10

3 a) £4.50   b) £5.70

4 a) £3.00   b) £3.50

5 a) 2   b) 4

Pages 16–17

1 a) 50
   b) 500
   c) 5000 (2 marks for all correct, 1 mark for 2 correct)

2 34

3 507, 570, 577, 705, 750, 755

4 378

5 147 and 145 **both** circled

6 25p, £0.65, 99p, £2, £2.35, £8

7 245

8 0.347, 0.374, 0.534, 0.7, 0.75, 0.753

9 a) 83   b) 4   c) 13   (1 mark for 2 correct, 2 marks for all correct)

10 a) 4.18, 4.20/4.2, 4.22
   b) 0.04, 0.05, 0.06
   c) 2.3, 2.7, 3.1
   (1 mark for 2 sequences correct, 2 marks for all correct)

11 8843

12 Answers in the range 165–175 inclusive

13 greatest = 244 km (1 mark); least = 235 (1 mark)

14 a) Emma
   b) 0.2 seconds (or 2/10 seconds)

15 1.82 m

Page 18

1 a) 3400   b) 350
   c) 100   d) 7200
   (2 marks for all correct; 1 mark for 2 or more correct)

2 a) 2700   b) 6000

3 a) 400 × 10 = 4000
   b) 30 × 100 = 3000

4 470

5 3500 m (or 3.5 km or $3\frac{1}{2}$ km)

6 5800

7 No. Multiplying 20 by 100 pushes the 20 two places to the left, leaving two places for zeros, making 2000.

Page 19

1 a) 10   b) 230
   c) 10   d) 380
   (2 marks for all correct; 1 mark for 2 or more correct)

2 a) 2   b) 40

3 a) 800 ÷ 100 = 8
   b) 500 ÷ 10 = 50

4 14

5 56,400p

6 30 days

7 670 m

8 No. Dividing 530,000 by 1000 pushes the 530,000 three places to the right, removing three zeros and making 530.

Page 20

1 3940

2 930

3 a) 267   b) 369

4 179

5 37 + 38

6 £461

7 £68 (2 marks for correct answer; 1 mark for evidence of correct working but incorrect answer)

Page 21

1 119

2 3737

3 72 and 34 both circled

4 a) 188   b) 611

5 157

6 £14

7 69

8 31 (2 marks for correct answer; 1 mark for evidence of correct working but incorrect answer)

9 £63

Page 22

1 a) 210   b) 608   c) 215   d) 558

2 a) 8   b) 54   c) 7   d) 85

3 a) >   b) >   c) <

4 1 × 100 or 2 × 50 or 4 × 25 or 5 × 20 or 10 × 10

5 a) 120   b) 165
   (2 marks each for correct answer, 1 mark for incorrect answer but evidence of correct working)

Page 23

1 a) 19   b) 18   c) 129   d) 14

2 a) 201   b) 4   c) 6   d) 301

3
   220 ÷ 4   84 ÷ 3 + 26

   2 × 108 ÷ 4   224 ÷ 4

   110 × 5 ÷ 10   140 ÷ 5 + 28

   (2 marks for all correct, 1 mark for 2 correct)

4 a) £22   b) £26   c) 17 days

Page 24

1 a) 11.1   b) 15   c) 2.9   d) 2.6

2 a) 19.7   b) 18.6

c) 39.85   d) 67.31

3 a) 16.80   b) 94.95
   c) 18.69   d) 37.86

4 <150 = d   >150 = a, b   = 150 = c
   (2 marks for all correct, 1 mark for 2 or 3 correct)

5 1.5 km

Page 25

1 a) 1:3 or 1 to every 3
   b) $\frac{1}{4}$ or 1 in every 4

2 a) 1:5 or 1 to every 5
   b) $\frac{5}{6}$ or 5 in every 6

3 a) 1:2 or 1 to every 2
   b) $\frac{4}{9}$ or 4 in every 9
   c) 1:2 or 1 to every 2
   d) $\frac{1}{9}$ or 1 in every 9

Pages 26–27

1 a) 350 + 400 = 750
   b) 570 – 240 = 330
   c) 60 × 10 = 600
   d) 750 ÷ 10 = 75

2 a) even   b) odd   c) even
   d) even   e) odd   f) even
   (2 correct for 1 mark, max 3 marks)

3 a) 356 + 134 = 490   490 – 356 = 134
      490 – 134 = 356   (all for 1 mark)
   b) 4 × 451 = 1804   1804 ÷ 4 = 451
      1804 ÷ 451 = 4   (all for 1 mark)
   c) 472 ÷ 59 = 8   59 × 8 = 472
      8 × 59 = 472   (all for 1 mark)

4 YES – 567 is an odd number and 368 is an even number. If you add an odd number and an even number you get an odd number.
   OR: 8 + 7 in the units is 15, so the answer will end in 5 and be an odd number.
   (up to 3 marks, depending on the clarity of the answer)

5 Multiplying a one-digit number by a two-digit number can't give a four-digit number.
   OR: 99 is the biggest two-digit number and 99 × 10 = 990, which is not a four-digit number (or similar).
   OR: He knows 4 × 25 = 100 and his answer is a lot bigger than that.
   (up to 3 marks, depending on the clarity of the answer)

6 Add from the top to the bottom and then the bottom to the top.
   OR: Add the numbers in a different order.
   OR: Round the numbers and add them.
   (NOT do the calculation again – this option is removed in the question).
   Michelle's answer is wrong. The correct answer is 840.
   (up to 2 marks per method, depending on the clarity of the answer)

Page 28

1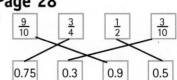
   (2 marks for all correct, 1 mark for 2 correct)

2 0.333333...

3 $\frac{4}{10}$ or $\frac{2}{5}$ or equivalent; 0.4 (1 mark each)

4 a) 9 pieces coloured
   b) $\frac{1}{10}$ and 0.1 (1 mark each)

5 none

A2

Page 29

1. a) $\frac{1}{2}$ or 50% or 0.5
   b) $\frac{1}{4}$ or 25% or 0.25
   c) $\frac{1}{10}$ or 10% or 0.1
   d) $\frac{2}{3}$ or 66% or 0.6 or 0.66
   e) $\frac{1}{3}$ or 33% or 0.3 or 0.33
2. cells completed correctly
   1 mark for each cell correct to a maximum of 12 marks

Fraction	Decimal	Percentage
	1.0	100%
$\frac{1}{2}$ or equivalent		50%
	0.1	10%
$\frac{1}{4}$ or equivalent	0.25	
$\frac{1}{100}$ or equivalent	0.01	
$\frac{3}{4}$ or equivalent		75%

Page 30

1. 1, 2, 3, 6, 9, 18
   (2 marks for all factors, 1 mark for 4 or 5 factors and no more than 1 incorrect)
2. 25
3. 7, 14, 21
4. a) 402
   b) The digits of the number add up to make a multiple of 3.
5. a) 9
   b) It is made by a 3 × 3 grid, which is square.
6.

	Multiples of 4	Not multiples of 4
Factors of 12	4, 12	1, 2, 3, 6
Not factors of 12	8	5, 7, 9, 10, 11

(2 marks for all correct; 1 mark for at least 8 numbers correctly placed)

Page 31

1. a) 13 cm   b) 23 cm
   c) 71 cm   d) 119 cm
2. The number of weeks multiplied by 7.
3. The number of boxes multiplied by 6.
4. The length of one side multiplied by 4.
5. The number of days multiplied by 24.

Pages 32–33

1. a) A (5, 8), B (8, 3), C (4, 0), D (1, 4), E (1, 1), F (2, 6) *(1 mark each)*
   b)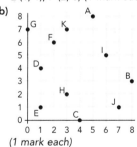
   (1 mark each)
2. a) Line from C ending at (4, 5)
   b) (4, 5) *(1 mark for each coordinate)*
3. a) (2, 8) OR one of: (5, 0), (5, 1), (5, 3), (5, 4), (5, 5), (5, 6), (5, 7) (5, 8)
   b) (2, 2)
4. (1, 1), (5, 1) and (5, 7) OR (1, 3), (7, 3) and (7, 7)
   (2 marks for all correct, 1 mark for 2 correct)
5. a) (2, 5)
   b) (3, 3) marked as D

Page 34

1. a) Equilateral; all sides and angles marked as equal
   b) Scalene; no sides or angles marked as equal
   c) Isosceles; 2 sides and 2 angles marked as equal
   (2 marks per triangle)
2. a) Triangles C and E marked with a cross
   b) Right angle marked in every triangle *(1 mark)*
3. side 2 = 6 cm   side 3 = 6 cm
   total of all sides = 18 cm *(3 marks, 1 mark each)*
4. One side as 10 cm and the other **not** 10 cm
   OR other 2 sides equal but **not** 10 cm
   (2 marks, 1 mark each)

Page 35

1. a) 12   b) 8
2. Four from:
   Two pairs of equal sides/opposite sides are equal
   4 sides
   4 right angles
   Two pairs of parallel lines
   Two pairs of perpendicular lines
   (4 marks, 1 for each property identified)
3.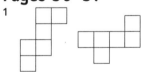
   (3 marks for all correct, 2 marks for 5 or more markings correct, 1 mark for 3 or more markings correct; deduct 1 mark for each incorrect marking)
4. Lines drawn parallel *(1 mark)*; lines 3 cm apart *(1 mark)*

Pages 36–37

1.
   These nets ticked *(1 mark each, deduct 1 mark for each incorrect answer)*
2. 2 triangles and 3 rectangles ticked
3. Sphere and cylinder *(1 mark each, deduct 1 mark for each incorrect answer)*
4. 6 faces, 8 vertices and 12 edges *(1 mark each)*
5. 5 rectangles and 1 hexagon drawn *(1 mark)*, Correctly positioned for a net *(1 mark)*
6. a)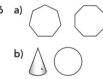
   b)
7. a) 25   b) 30
8. a) 9   b) 22

Page 38

1. Angles B and D circled *(1 mark each, deduct 1 mark for each incorrect answer)*
2. B and C circled, A and E crossed out *(3 marks for all correct, 2 marks for 3 correct and 1 mark for 2 correct; deduct 1 mark for each incorrect angle)*
3. D, B, E, A, C

4a) and 4b): *(2 marks each for correct answer, 1 mark for evidence of correct working but incorrect answer)*
4. a) 35°   b) 59°

Page 39

1. 120 cm
2. a) 4 cm
   b) 20 cm
3. Rectangle drawn 8 cm by 5 cm *(1 mark for correct length, 1 mark for correct breadth, 1 mark for straight lines accurately drawn)*

Pages 40–41

1.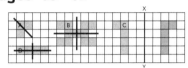
   a) Lines as shown *(1 mark for each correct line, deduct 1 mark for each incorrect line)*
   b) Reflection as shown above *(2 marks correct, 1 mark for right shape in wrong position)*
2.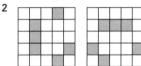
   (2 marks for each correct tile; 1 mark per tile if at least 3 squares shaded correctly)
3.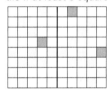
   (1 mark for each square correctly shaded; deduct 1 mark for each square incorrectly shaded)
4.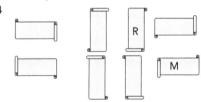
   (1 mark for each letter)
5.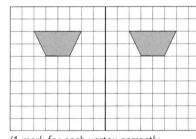
   (1 mark for each vertex correctly positioned)

Page 42

1. 20 cm
2. 32 cm
3. a) E   b) B and D
4. 24 cm
5 and 6: *(2 marks each for correct answer, 1 mark for evidence of correct working but incorrect answer)*
5. 5 cm
6. 4 cm

Page 43

1 a) 9 cm²
   b) 18 cm² *(2 marks each for correct answer, 1 mark for evidence of correct working but incorrect answer)*
   c) 12 cm²
2a) to 2c): *(2 marks each for correct answer, 1 mark for evidence of correct working but incorrect answer)*
2 a) 8 cm²   b) 15 cm²   c) 20 cm²
3 6 m²
4 40 m²

Page 44

1 86 mm
2

(2 marks for all correct, 1 mark for 2 correct)
3 a) 5000 g   b) 3000 ml   c) 200 mm
   d) 50 m   e) 8000 mm   f) $\frac{1}{2}$ or 0.5 kg
   (1 mark for every 3 correct answers – maximum 2 marks)
4 a) Fact Finders
   b) 1 hour and 55 minutes *(2 marks for correct answer, 1 mark for incorrect answer but evidence of correct working)*
   c) 15 minutes
   d) Top Marks

Page 45

1 a) A = 20, B = 45, C = 7–9 inclusive *(2 marks for all correct, 1 mark for 2 correct)*
   b) arrow between 30 and 33 inclusive
2 a) D = 140, E = 190, F = 121–125 inclusive *(2 marks for all correct, 1 mark for 2 correct)*
   b) arrow between 152 and 158 inclusive
3 a) 70 ml
   b) 1600 ml or 1.6 litres or 1 litre 600 ml
   c) 3.5 litres or 3500 ml or 3 litres 500 ml
4

1800   1900   2000

Pages 46–47

1 a) 4:20 or 20 past 4
   b) 3:30 or $\frac{1}{2}$ past 3
   c) 5:58 or 2 minutes to 6
   d) 9:10 or 10 past 9
2 a) 3:40 or 20 to 4
   b) 6:15 or $\frac{1}{4}$ past 6
   c) 10:55 or 5 to 11
   d) 12:05 or 5 past 12
3 a) 8:16 or 16 past 8
   b) 17 minutes
   c) 31 minutes
   d) 25 minutes
   e) in the last column 9:50, 9:56, 10:04, 10:21 *(1 mark for each except 9:50)*
4 a) $\frac{1}{4}$ past 8 or 8:15
   b) i) 2 a.m.
      ii) It is the middle of the night in London – her sister will be in bed!

Pages 48–49

1 a) 16–18 (inclusive)
   b) 1:30 p.m. and 5:30 p.m. (+/– 10 minutes)

c) 3 p.m. and 6 p.m.
d) 16
e) There are children there in the afternoon, so it can't be a school day. *(2 marks)*
2 a)

(award up to 3 marks)
   b) Tuesday and Wednesday
   c) That's when he learnt the most tricks.
3 a) August   b) March and October
   c) 18°C (+/– 1)
   d) It increased till May, then fell in June, rose till August and then decreased quite sharply through to December. *(2 marks for comprehensive description; 1 mark for creditable attempt)*

Pages 50–51

1 a) Check graphs drawn and award up to 4 marks for neatness and accuracy. Groups should have a range of about 5, in which case 0–4 is the most common for **1b**.
2 a) India
   b) 26–27 minutes (inclusive)
   c) 12–13 minutes *(2 marks)*
   d) 392 minutes (+/– 10 minutes) *(2 marks)*
   e) Check graphs drawn and award up to 4 marks for neatness and accuracy. Groups should have a range of about 5, in which case 10–15 is most common for **2f**.

Page 52

1 a) range = 2   mode = 4
   b) range = 2.2   mode = 8.4
   c) range = 288   mode = 612
2 a) No, because the largest number was 65 and the smallest was 41; 65 − 41 = 24, so the range is 24. *(2 marks for correct answer, 1 mark for partial answer)*
   b) 53 minutes

Page 53

1 a) 11, 14, 17   Rule: add 3 *(2 marks)*
   b) 5, 3, 1   Rule: subtract 2 *(2 marks)*
2 a) 5, 9, 13, 17, 21   b) 20, 14, 8, 2, −4
   c) 1, 4, 10, 22, 46
3 a) 11, 7   b) 13, 19   c) 16, 27

Pages 54–56

1 a) £26.49   b) £7.02
2 3.64 kg
3 a) 2.8 litres   b) 1.4 litres
4 It costs £6.50 to get to Whitehall. A climbing session costs £9.80. *(1 mark each, deduct 1 mark for each statement ticked incorrectly)*
5 and **6**: *(2 marks each for correct answer, 1 mark for evidence of correct working but incorrect answer)*
5 £13.80 (NOT £13.8)
6 294p or £2.94
7 66 × 2 = 132 or 22 × 6 = 132
8 £112 *(2 marks for correct answer, 1 mark for incorrect answer but evidence of correct working)*

9 a) Cross out 'She gets £1.50 pocket money a week. She reads the magazine over 3 days.'
   b) 594p or £5.94 *(2 marks for correct answer, 1 mark for incorrect answer but evidence of correct working)*
10a) and **10b**): *(2 marks each for correct answer, 1 mark for evidence of correct working but incorrect answer)*
10 a) 392 kilometres
    b) 399 minutes or 6 hours and 39 minutes
11 a) 19   b) 21
12 a) 50   b) 130
13 a) 17   b) 13   c) 26

Page 57

1 and **2a**): *(2 marks each for correct answer, 1 mark for evidence of correct working but incorrect answer)*
1 a) 1.37 p.m.   b) 42   c) 13
2 a) 50
   b) 1.2 kg or 1200 g
3 a) 8.49 km   b) 3.19 km   c) 7.95 km

Page 58

1 a)

   b) pentagon   c) 1
2 Example:

   *(Make sure there are only **two** pairs of perpendicular lines.)*
3 semi-circle (or crescent)
4 a) 20 cm   b) 10 cm   c) 60 cm

Page 59

1 a) 27.08 m
   b) 3.99 m between years 3 and 4 *(2 marks for correct answer, 1 mark for incorrect answer but evidence of correct working)*
   c) Year 3
2 a) Tuesday 30, Thursday 46–48 inclusive *(1 mark each)*
   b) Wednesday
   c) Because just a few books were taken out.
   d) 9 whole books drawn and about $\frac{1}{3}$ of a book

Page 60

1 Because 8 × 30p is 240p which is £2.40
2 a) Isaac
   b) 6 × 50 km = 300 km so that's 6 hours
3 a) No   b) 6
   c) 10 × 6 = 60 minutes and 60 minutes = 1 hour

Using simple formulae

Checking your understanding

1 To find the length of his photos Ben has to use the formula **double the width and add 3**.

Find out the length of his photo if the width is:

a) 5 cm

> 1a
> 1 mark

b) 10 cm

> 1b
> 1 mark

c) 34 cm

> 1c
> 1 mark

d) 58 cm

> 1d
> 1 mark

Using and applying

2 Write the formula for finding the number of days in any number of weeks.

> 2
> 1 mark

3 Write the formula for finding the number of eggs in any number of egg boxes.

> 3
> 1 mark

4 Write the formula for finding the perimeter of a square.

> 4
> 1 mark

5 Write the formula for finding the number of hours in any number of days.

> 5
> 1 mark

Total marks for this topic

31

Using coordinates

Checking your understanding

1

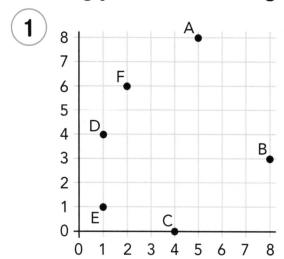

a) Write the coordinates of the points plotted on the grid.

A = [ ]   B = [ ]   C = [ ]

D = [ ]   E = [ ]   F = [ ]

b) Mark and label these points on the grid:

G (0, 7)   H (3, 2)   I (6, 5)   J (7, 1)   K (3, 7)

Using and applying

2

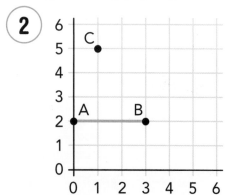

a) Draw a line from point C that is parallel to and equal to line AB.
Label the end of the line D.

b) What are the coordinates of point D? [ ]

1a
6 marks

1b
5 marks

2a
2 marks

2b
1 mark

3

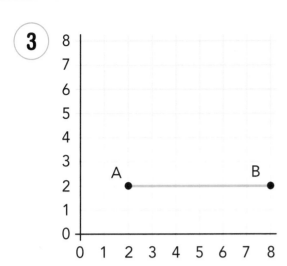

a) Mark point C on the grid so that points A, B and C can be joined to make an isosceles triangle. Join the points to show the triangle.

3a

1 mark

b) Write the coordinates of point A.

3b

1 mark

4

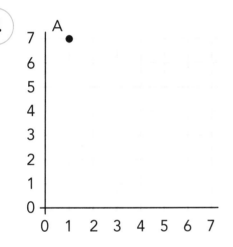

Mark the coordinates so that point A is part of a 6 by 4 rectangle.

4

2 marks

5

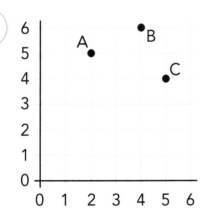

a) What are the coordinates of A?

5a

1 mark

b) Mark point D so the shape ABCD is a square.

5b

1 mark

Total marks for this topic

33

2-D shapes

Checking your understanding

1 Name the triangles and mark all equal angles and equal sides on the triangles.

a)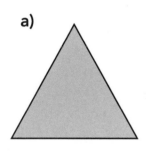

b)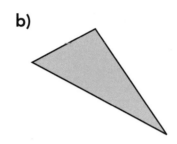

c)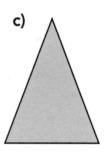

a)

b)

c)

6 marks 1

2 A 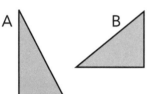 B 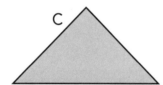 C D E

a) Mark each isosceles triangle with a cross.

b) Mark all the right angles in the triangles.

1 mark 2a

1 mark 2b

Using and applying

3 An equilateral triangle has one side of 6 cm. Write the length of its other sides and the total of all three sides.

side 2 = [ ]   side 3 = [ ]

total of all sides = [ ]

3 marks 3

4 An isosceles triangle has one side of length 10 cm. What might be the length of the other two sides?

side 2 = [ ]   side 3 = [ ]

2 marks 4

Total marks for this topic [ ]

Properties of other 2-D shapes

Checking your understanding

1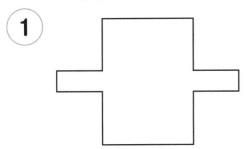

a) This shape has [ ] sides.

1a
[ ]
1 mark

b) There are [ ] right angles inside the shape.

1b
[ ]
1 mark

2 List four properties of a rectangle.

a) [ ]

b) [ ]

c) [ ]

d) [ ]

2
[ ]
4 marks

3 Circle all quadrilaterals and put a cross on each regular shape.

3
[ ]
3 marks

Using and applying

4 Use a set square to draw a pair of parallel lines 3 cm apart.

4
[ ]
2 marks

Total marks for this topic [ ]

35

3-D shapes

Checking your understanding

1 Tick the nets that will make cubes.

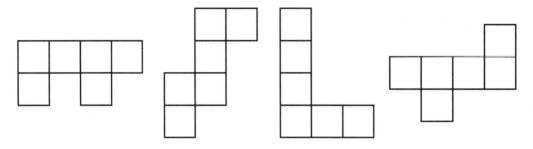

	1
	2 marks

2 Tick the shapes needed to build a triangular prism.

	2
	1 mark

3 Circle the 3-D shapes that have any curved surfaces.

cube   sphere   prism   cylinder   pyramid

	3
	2 marks

4 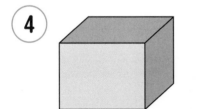 A cuboid has ☐ faces, ☐ vertices

and ☐ edges.

	4
	3 marks

5 Complete the net for a hexagonal prism. Draw the net on a separate sheet of paper.

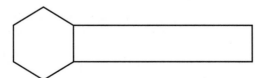

	5
	2 marks

Using and applying

6 Add two more shapes to each of these patterns.

a)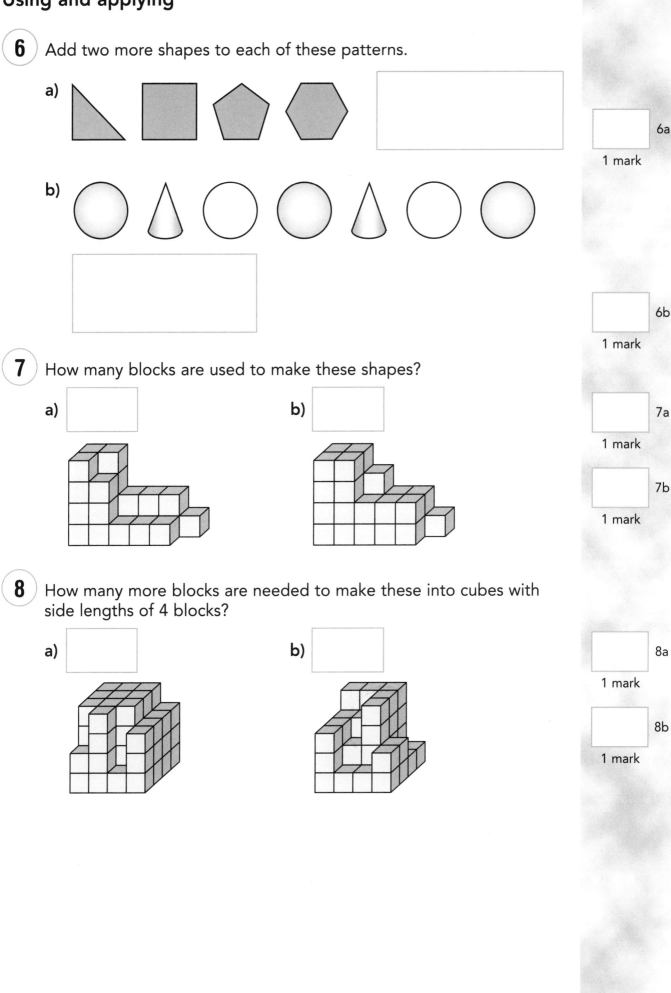

6a

1 mark

b)

6b

1 mark

7 How many blocks are used to make these shapes?

a)

b)

7a

1 mark

7b

1 mark

8 How many more blocks are needed to make these into cubes with side lengths of 4 blocks?

a)

b)

8a

1 mark

8b

1 mark

Total marks for this topic

37

Angles

Checking your understanding

1 Circle the angles that are more than 180°.

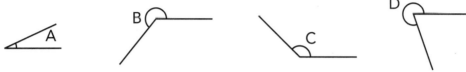

2 marks   1

2

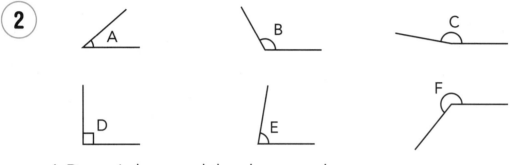

a) Draw circles round the obtuse angles.

b) Put crosses through the acute angles.

3 marks   2

3 Put the angles in order, starting with the largest.

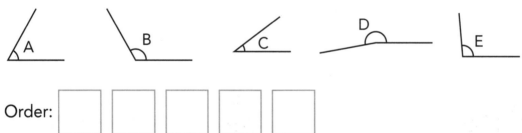

Order: ☐ ☐ ☐ ☐ ☐

1 mark   3

Using and applying

4 Calculate the size of the angles marked x.

a)

2 marks   4a

b)

2 marks   4b

Total marks for this topic

Drawing 2-D and 3-D shapes to scale

1 This line is drawn using a scale of 1 cm for every 20 cm.

_____

What is the length of the real line? [ ]

1

1 mark

2 This is a scale drawing of a book.
1 cm is drawn for every 5 cm long the book is.

length

a) Measure the length of the drawing. [ ]

2a

1 mark

b) What is the length of the real book? [ ]

2b

1 mark

Using and applying

3 A piece of paper is 80 cm long and 50 cm wide. Use a ruler and a right angle measure to make a scale drawing using 1 cm for every 10 cm.

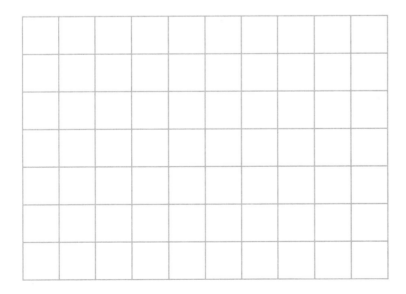

3

3 marks

Total marks for this topic [ ]

39

Moving 2-D shapes

Checking your understanding

1 Look at the shapes in the grid.

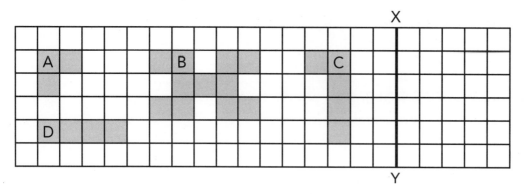

a) Mark all the lines of symmetry on these shapes.

b) Draw the reflection of shape C in the mirror line XY.

1a

5 marks

1b

2 marks

2 Continue the pattern made by turning the tile clockwise.

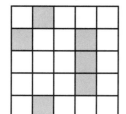 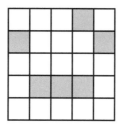 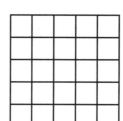 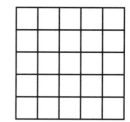

2

4 marks

3 Colour three more squares to make this into a symmetrical pattern.

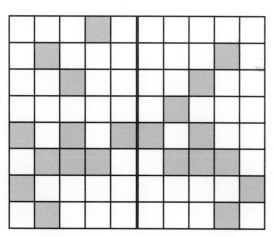

3

3 marks

4 Look at shape A.

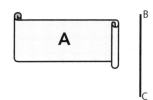

a) Write **R** on the diagram below that shows that shape after a clockwise rotation of 90°.

b) Write **M** on the diagram below that shows the shape after it has been reflected in the mirror line BC.

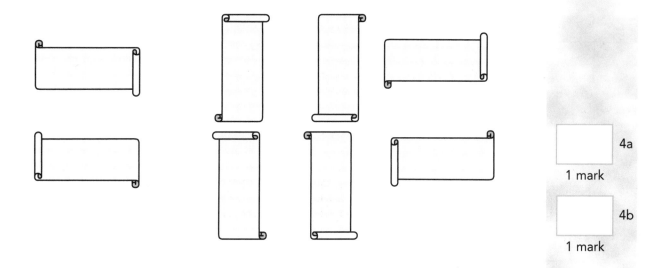

	4a
1 mark	

	4b
1 mark	

5 Reflect the shape in the mirror line.

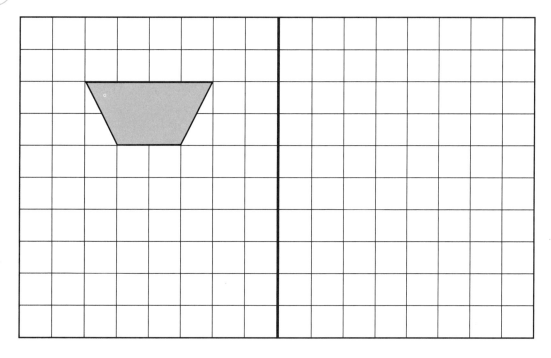

	5
4 marks	

Total marks for this topic

41

Perimeters of simple shapes

Checking your understanding

1 What is the perimeter of this pentagon?

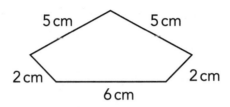

5 cm   5 cm
2 cm   2 cm
6 cm

2 What is the perimeter of this square?

8 cm

3 Look at the shapes on the grid.

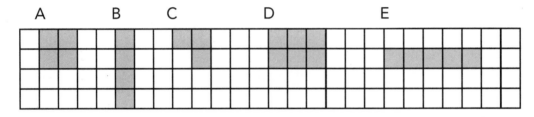

A   B   C   D   E

a) Which of these shapes has the largest perimeter?

b) Which two shapes each have a perimeter of 10?

Using and applying

4 A regular hexagon has a side length of 4 cm.

What is its perimeter?

5 A regular octagon has a perimeter of 40 cm.

What is the length of one side?

6 A rectangle has a perimeter of 12 cm. If one side is 2 cm long, what is the length of the longer side?

Total marks for this topic

Areas of simple shapes

Checking your understanding

1 Calculate the areas of the black shapes. 1 square = 1 cm

a) 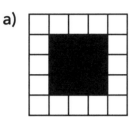 **b)** 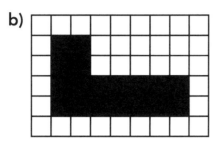 **c)**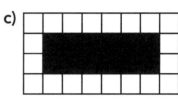

a)  **b)**  **c)**

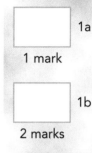
2 What are the areas of these rectangles?

a) 2 cm 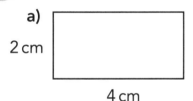 4 cm

b) 5 cm 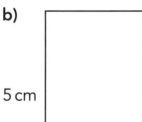 3 cm

c) 4 cm 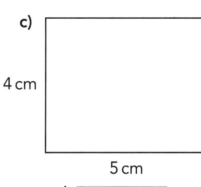 5 cm

a)

b)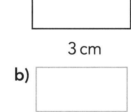

c)

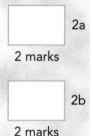
Using and applying

3 A PE mat is 2 m long and 3 m wide. What is its area?

4 A room is 10 m long and 4 m wide. What area of carpet is needed to cover the floor?

Total marks for this topic

Measures

Checking your understanding

1 Measure this line to the nearest mm.

_____ [ ] mm

1

1 mark

2 Match the times that are the same.

2

2 marks

3 a) 5 kg = [ ] g

b) 3 litres = [ ] ml

c) 20 cm = [ ] mm

d) 5000 cm = [ ] m

e) 8 m = [ ] mm

f) 500 g = [ ] kg

3

2 marks

Using and applying

4 Emma looks at the TV programmes on CCB for the evening.

4:50	Us It or Lose It
5:15	Top Marks
5:50	Fact Finders
6:10	Rising Stars (film)
8:05	Bright Lights
9:00	Homework Heroes

a) Which programme starts at 10 to 6?

[   ]

4a

1 mark

b) How long does the film 'Rising Stars' last?

[   ]

4b

2 marks

c) Emma has band after school. She gets home at 5 past 5. How much of 'Use It or Lose It' has she missed?

[   ]

4c

1 mark

d) Which programme lasts 35 minutes?

[   ]

4d

1 mark

Total marks for this topic

[   ]

Reading scales

Checking your understanding

1

a) Write the number pointed at by each arrow.

A = ☐   B = ☐   C = ☐

1a
2 marks

b) Draw an arrow to show where the number 31 would be on the number line.

1b
1 mark

2

a) Write the number pointed at by each arrow.

D = ☐   E = ☐   F = ☐

2a
2 marks

b) Draw an arrow to show where the number 155 would be on the number line.

2b
1 mark

Using and applying

3 Write the amount of water in each of these measuring jugs.

a) 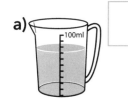 ☐   b) 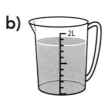 ☐   c) ☐

3
3 marks

4 Mark 1924 on this time line.

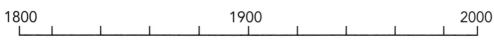

4
1 mark

Total marks for this topic ☐

45

Time and timetables

1 **a)** What time is it 10 minutes after 10 past 4? ☐

b) What time is it 2 hours before 5:30? ☐

c) What time is it 2 minutes before 6 o'clock? ☐

d) What time is it 20 minutes after 10 to 9? ☐

2 What time is it 25 minutes after these times?

a)

☐

b)

☐

c)

☐

d)

☐

Using and applying

3 This is a timetable for the train at Chinley.

Chinley	7:20	7:45	8:10	8:30	9:05	
New Mills	7:26	7:51	8:16	8:36	9:11	
Marple	7:34	7:59	8:24	8:44	9:19	
Stockport	7:51	8:16	8:41	9:01	9:36	

a) What time is the first train after 8 o'clock at New Mills?

3a
1 mark

b) How long is the journey from Marple to Stockport?

3b
1 mark

c) How long is the journey from Chinley to Stockport?

3c
1 mark

d) George just misses the 7:45 at Chinley. How long does he have to wait for the next train?

3d
1 mark

e) The next train from Chinley after 9:05 is at 9:50. Fill in the last column to show the times this train calls at all the stations.

3e
3 marks

4 The time in Mexico City is 6 hours behind the time in London.

London

Mexico City

a) If it is $\frac{1}{4}$ past 2 in London, what time is it in Mexico City?

4a
1 mark

b) Emanuela lives in Mexico City. Her sister lives in London. Emanuela phones her sister at 8 p.m., Mexico City time.

i) What time is it in London when she phones?

4bi
1 mark

ii) Why might this be a problem?

4bii
1 mark

Total marks for this topic

47

Line graphs

Using and applying

1 Dominik counts the number of children at the skate park for each hour.

Number of children at the skate park

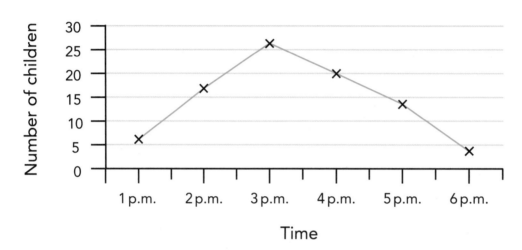

a) How many children were at the skate park at 2 p.m.?

1 mark | 1a

b) At what times were there about 10 children at the park?

1 mark | 1b

c) Between which times does the number of children decrease?

1 mark | 1c

d) How many fewer are in the skate park at 6 p.m. than at 4 p.m.?

1 mark | 1d

e) Ali says, 'Dominik was counting on a Saturday'. Explain how and why the graph supports his opinion.

2 marks | 1e

2 This is the number of tricks Dan can do:

Monday   2

Tuesday   8

Wednesday   17

Thursday   23

Friday   31

a) Plot this information on the line graph.

2a   3 marks

b) Between which two days is the line steepest?

2b   1 mark

c) Explain why.

2c   1 mark

3 The pupils at Newtown School kept a record of the average monthly temperature for one year. They presented their results as a line graph.

Average monthly temperature

Temperature (°C) vs Month

a) In which month was the average temperature highest?

3a   1 mark

b) In which months was the average temperature 10°C?

3b   1 mark

c) What was the average temperature in May?

3c   1 mark

d) Explain what happened to the average temperature over the year.

3d   2 marks

Total marks for this topic

49

Grouping data

Checking your understanding

1 The Dingbats count how many planets they each visit in a year. They present the information on a bar chart.

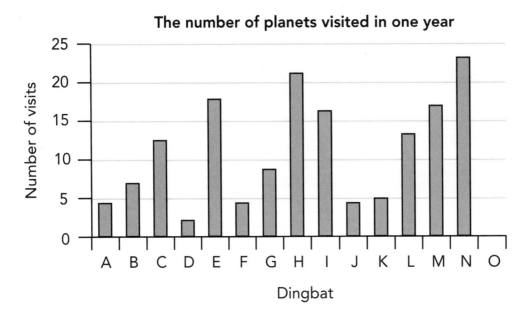

The number of planets visited in one year

a) The Chief Dingbat asks for the data to be grouped. Decide how to group the data and complete another graph to show the information.

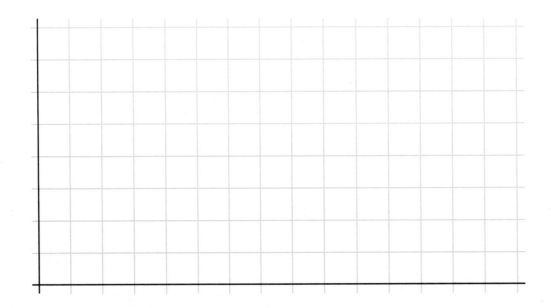

b) Which is the most common group?

1a

4 marks

1b

1 mark

2 KS2 children were working out how much exercise they do each day. One group worked out how long they spent walking home and made a bar chart of their findings.

Time spent walking home

Name of pupil

a) Who spent the longest time walking home?

b) How long did Emma spend walking home?

c) How much longer did Josh spend walking than Dan?

d) What was the total number of minutes the group spent walking?

e) Mr Mansell asks for the data to be grouped. Decide how to group the data and complete another graph to show the information.

f) Which is the most common group?

Total marks for this topic

Finding the range and mode

Checking your understanding

1 Find the range and mode of these sets of numbers.

a) 5, 4, 3, 4, 5, 3, 4

Range =

Mode =

1a

2 marks

b) 7.1, 8.4, 9.2, 7, 7.3, 7.8, 8.4

Range =

Mode =

1b

2 marks

c) 324, 419, 612, 376, 425, 612, 384

Range =

Mode =

1c

2 marks

Using and applying

2 This table shows how long a group of children each spent on the Internet yesterday.

Name	James	Dawa	Sam	Hannah	Emma	Safi	Leah
Time (in minutes)	53	57	65	53	51	41	56

a) James says the range was 25 minutes.

Is James correct?   YES   NO

Explain how you know.

2a

2 marks

b) What is the mode of the time spent on the computer?

2b

1 mark

Total marks for this topic

Number patterns

Checking your understanding

1 Write the next three numbers in these sequences and write the rule for making the sequence.

a) 2, 5, 8, ☐ , ☐ , ☐

Rule: ☐

☐	1a

2 marks

b) 11, 9, 7, ☐ , ☐ , ☐

Rule: ☐

☐	1b

2 marks

2 Follow these rules to write the first five numbers in these sequences.

a) Start with 5, and add 4 to get each number after that.

☐ , ☐ , ☐ , ☐ , ☐

☐	2a

1 mark

b) Start with 20 and subtract 6 to get each number after that.

☐ , ☐ , ☐ , ☐ , ☐

☐	2b

1 mark

c) Start with 1. Double the number and add 2 to get the next number each time.

☐ , ☐ , ☐ , ☐ , ☐

☐	2c

1 mark

3 In each sequence the same number is added or subtracted each time. Fill in the missing numbers.

☐	3a

1 mark

a) 15, ☐ , ☐ , 3

☐	3b

1 mark

b) 7, ☐ , ☐ , 25

☐	3c

1 mark

c) 5, ☐ , ☐ , 38

Total marks for this topic ☐

53

Solving number problems

1 Sam bought a headphone set and a webcam for his computer. The headphone set cost £16.49 and he paid £42.98 altogether.

a) How much did the webcam cost?

1a

1 mark

b) He paid with a £50 note. How much change did he get?

1b

1 mark

2 A bag of apples weighs 1.36 kg. How much is this less than 5 kg?

2

1 mark

3 India put 1.3 litres of water into a bucket. Leah added enough water to fill the bucket up to 4.1 litres.

a) How much water did Leah add?

3a

1 mark

b) India then tipped 2.7 litres of the water into a watering can. How much water was left in the bucket?

3b

1 mark

4 Josh wants to know how much it will cost him to go climbing at Whitehall.

Tick the boxes to show what information he will need.

The instructor gets paid £10 a session. ☐

It costs £6.50 to get to Whitehall. ☐

It takes 20 minutes to get to Whitehall. ☐

Ten people can take part in each climbing session. ☐

A climbing session costs £9.80. ☐

4

2 marks

5 Cyla got £20 for her birthday. She paid £4.55 for a train journey to Chinley, spent £6.25 on a meal and had to borrow £4.60 to pay for a horse-riding lesson. How much did the riding lesson cost?

5

2 marks

6 Kani buys himself and six friends a chocolate bar each. If the chocolate bars cost 42p each, how much did he spend altogether?

6

2 marks

7 Use the digits 2 and 6 to complete this calculation.

☐☐ × ☐ = 1 3 ☐

7

1 mark

8 It costs £4 for each child in Class 3 to go on a trip to Outdoor Action. If there are 28 children in the class, what is the total cost?

8

2 marks

9 Rachel buys a magazine every week for 6 weeks. She gets £1.50 pocket money a week. She reads the magazine over 3 days. The magazine costs 99p.

Rachel wants to know how much money she spends on the magazine.

a) Cross out the information in the question that she does **not** need to answer the question.

9a

1 mark

b) How much did Rachel spend?

9b

2 marks

10 It is 28 kilometres from Tegan's house to Manchester. She catches the train to Manchester and back every day for one week.

a) How far does she travel altogether?

10a

3 marks

b) If she spends 57 minutes a day on the train, what is the total time she spends travelling?

10b

3 marks

11 Six scouts go on a camping trip to the Lake District. There are 114 pieces of equipment to carry equally. They each have to carry the equipment in their backpacks.

a) If each scout carries the same number of pieces, how many must they each carry?

b) If two of the scouts carry 15 pieces of equipment each and the others share the rest of the equipment, how many pieces would they have to carry?

12 Buxworth School has a disco at the end of term. The pupils decide to use the money raised from the disco to help pay for a school trip next term. It costs each child 60p to attend the school disco.

a) If £30 is taken, how many children attended?

b) 40p from every person goes into the school fund. If the school wants to raise £52, how many people need to come to the disco?

13 New Mills swimming pool holds a special event in the school holidays. All children are allowed a free swimming session. At each pool session, 50 children are allowed in the pool.

a) If 850 children want to go swimming, how many pool sessions will be needed?

b) The pool is 25 m long. If Daniel swims 325 m, how many lengths has he swum?

c) Kadhi wants to swim 650 m. How many lengths does he need to swim?

Total marks for this topic

Solving measures problems

1   **a)** BOWLUP! is an 18-minute drive from school. Class 6 books five lanes from 2:10 p.m. If shoe hire takes 15 minutes, what is the latest time they should leave school?
Show your method.

	1a

2 marks

   b) At the café, Class 6 spent £50.40 on fruit shakes. If each fruit shake costs £1.20, how many did they buy? Show your method.

	1b

2 marks

   c) In a class of 30 children, 8 children use 4-kg balls, 9 children use 5-kg balls and the rest use 6-kg balls. How many children use 6-kg balls? Show your method.

	1c

2 marks

2   One gremlin weighs 40 g.

   a) If you want 2 kg of gremlins, how many gremlins would you need?

	2a

2 marks

   b) If you had 30 gremlins, what would they weigh?

	2b

1 mark

3

Whaley Bridge — 2.65 km — Furness Vale — 5.84 km — Newtown

   a) How far is it from Whaley Bridge to Newtown?

	3a

1 mark

   b) How much further is it to go to Newtown from Furness Vale than is it to go to Whaley Bridge from Furness Vale?

	3b

1 mark

   c) What is the distance from Furness Vale to Buxworth if it is three times the distance from Whaley Bridge to Furness Vale?

	3c

1 mark

Total marks for this topic

Solving shape problems

1 These are the diagonals of a shape.

a) Complete the shape.

b) The shape is a [_____].

c) It has [_____] lines of symmetry.

1a [____] 1 mark

1b [____] 1 mark

1c [____] 1 mark

2 Use the dots to draw a hexagon with two pairs of perpendicular lines.

2 [____] 1 mark

3 Michelle is thinking of a shape. It is not a polygon. It has two sides.

What is it? [_____]

3 [____] 1 mark

4 A circle has a diameter of 10 cm. Two of the circles just fit inside a rectangle.

10 cm

a) What is the length of the rectangle? [_____]

4a [____] 1 mark

b) What is the width of the rectangle? [_____]

4b [____] 1 mark

c) What is the perimeter of the rectangle? [_____]

4c [____] 1 mark

Total marks for this topic [____]

Solving data handling problems

1 After sports day, Sam makes a table showing the distance throw record over 4 years.

Year	Record (m)
1	26.54
2	27.02
3	27.08
4	31.07

a) What was the record in Year 3?

1a
1 mark

b) What was the greatest annual increase?

1b
2 marks

c) In which year was there a 0.06 m increase?

1c
1 mark

2 The pictogram shows how many books are taken out of the library each day.

Monday

Tuesday

Key
= 10 books

Wednesday

Thursday

Friday

Saturday

2a
2 marks

a) About how many books were taken out on these days?

Tuesday [ ]   Thursday [ ]

2b
1 mark

b) Which day do you think the library was open for only half a day?

2c
1 mark

c) Explain why. [ ]

2d
1 mark

d) On Saturday 93 books were taken out. Draw the symbols needed to show this.

Total marks for this topic [ ]

59

Check problems by context

1 Alex buys 8 trading cards for 30p each.

Libby

Alex: That will cost £6.

Alex

Libby: That can't be right!

How does Libby know that his answer isn't correct?

1

1 mark

2 A car is travelling at 50 km an hour. It travels for 300 km.

Rachel

Isaac: That will take 6 hours.

Isaac

Rachel: No – it will take 15 hours.

a) Who is correct?

2a

1 mark

b) Explain how you know.

2b

1 mark

3 It takes Olivia 10 minutes to walk round the park.

Olivia: I could walk round the park 10 times in 1 hour.

George: Mmm – how many minutes make an hour?

Olivia   *George*

a) Is Olivia correct?

3a

1 mark

b) How many times could she walk round the park in 1 hour?

3b

1 mark

c) Explain how you know.

3c

1 mark

Total marks for this topic
